MW00604414

Contents

Copyright Notice

Disclaimer Notice

All subjects in the interviews, their identities and names have been excluded for their privacy and safety. No part of this book is intended to replace medical, legal, or professional mental help related to any possible topic, subject, issue, or element within this book. Although the author and publisher have made every effort to ensure that the information in this book was correct at press time, the author and publisher do not assume and hereby disclaim any liability to any party for any loss, damage or disruption caused by error, omissions, or analysis, whether such errors result from negligence, accident, or any other cause. Any resemblance to actual persons, living or dead, or actual events is purely coincidental.

ISBN: 978-1-953059-17-8

PUBLISHER

THE AI ORGANIZATION

4275 Executive Square, Suite 200, La Jolla, California, 92037
www.THEAIORGANIZATION.com
Consult@Theaiorganization.com

ABOUT: THE AI ORGANIZATION

The AI Organization specializes in research, design, development, risk assessment and vulnerability consultation of Humanoid Robots, Micro-Botics, AI & Robotic Terrorism, AI Automated Drones, AI Automated Assassination Prevention, AI Bioengineering, AI Genetic Modification, AI Automated Cybernetics, AI Automated Cloning, AI Automated Animal-Human Hybrid System Detection, AI Automated Security Systems, AI, Scanning Apparatus, AI Detecting Apparatus, IoT, Smart Home, Smart City, Virtual Reality, Augmented Reality, Mixed Reality, Alternate Reality, Hologram Apparatus, The Human Bio-Digital Network, Bio-Digital Field, Bio-Matter, General Bio-Metrics, Facial Recognition, Voice Recognition, Human Body Detection Apparatus, Lidar, Machine Learning, Deep Learning (DL), (Artificial Intelligence (AI), Artificial Intelligence Nanotechnology, Artificial General Intelligence (AGI), Super Intelligence, the AI Global Bio-Digital Network and Military, Political and Governmental AI Risk & Operating Procedures for Prevention, Emergency & Response.

ABOUT: Cyrus A. Parsa

Cyrus A. Parsa, is the Founder and CEO of The AI Organization, where he is also Director of Creative Analysis & Defensive Innovations. He has researched and investigated more than 1,000 AI, Robotics, 5G, Cybernetic and Big Tech companies. Cyrus has a B.S. in International Security, Master's degree in Homeland Security, and lived with Buddhist-Taoist fighting monks in the mountains of China studying internal Wudang arts and meditation. He is an expert in AI, Quantum, 5G, Security, China and Iran affairs.

In summer of 2019, and early 2020, Cyrus predicted, and warned accurately in numerous way's that the world's people were in impending danger from a Disease or Bioweapon (Coronavirus) from China CCP that would lead to conflicts, AI enslavement, famines, misuse of biotech, civil

wars, deaths, and world wars. Cyrus provided

solutions as remedy.

June 2019, Secret Service 5 Page Brief: MBT (Bioweapon, Poison) from China within 6 months-1 Year, then global enslavement within 1-2 years.

June 15th, 62 Page Report to Fmr. CIA Director of Covert-Ops, China threatens the worlds citizens with AI and Bioweapons.

*August 24th, 2019, Published the book AI, Trump, China and the Weaponization of Robotics with 5G. First sentence in Synopsis: World in Danger, China CCP and Big tech Threaten all the world citizens with Micro-Botic Terrorism (Poison, Virus, Bioweapon) and AI enslavement.

*October 20th, 2020, Bestselling AI book: _Artificial Intelligence Dangers to Humanity_**. China-Big Tech threaten world with MBT (Poison, Virus, Bioweapon), AI enslavement, listed 50 companies.**

Cyrus is also the author of a rape-human trafficking prevention book called Raped via Bio-Digital Social Programming. Cyrus is also the producer of the

Documentary CCP Virus Gate: The plan to stop China CCP's AI Extinction Agenda and the creator of the movie AI: The Plan to Invade Humanity.

Cyrus's mission is to help safeguard humanity first, and prevent disasters to the world's people from China, Big Tech and the misuse of AI and biotechnology. He also runs Loyal Guardian Security, which specializes in China and Iran Intelligence and risk assessment created to assist in making our society safer and better.

He is an expert in US, China & Iran affairs, and has consulted on Human-Organ Tracking, Anti-Terrorism, Vulnerability, Risk Assessments, Asset Management and Emerging Threats to governments, agencies, people and organizations. He also speaks Chinese, Persian, and English. With 20 years of hidden research and development in his consultation work, he assesses & provides guidance for clients from a multi-dimensional and multi-layered perspective. He maintains networks of thousands of Chinese and Western influencers and intelligence assets, allowing for great insight into the threats we face from China, Iran and the Western inter-connectivity of these countries. To know more, visit: https://theaiorganiztion.com/about-Cyrus-A-Parsa/

SOURCE FOR ANALYSIS OF "GREAT RESET"

We were able to accurately predict and warn about COVID 19 (AKA Bioweapon/CCP Virus) from China, the lockdown, and thousands of interconnected events and threats prior to their occurrence on the world stage. The analysis in this book is derived from compressing the data, experience, reports, and intel from Cyrus A. Parsa, and The AI Organization's network of intelligence teams.

Our findings in 2019 was ahead of the CIA, FBI, NSA, Secret Service, DHS, Pentagon, and more accurate than Bill Gates and the World Economic Forum's pandemic simulations. As we knew the year, month, origin, Bioengineering "mixing humans with animals", and so many other aspects prior to it occurring. All documented in Secret Service reports, report to Fmr. Head of CIA Covert Ops, Book AI Trump, China and the Weaponization of Robotics with 5G, and bestselling book, Artificial Intelligence Dangers to Humanity, federal disclosures, and various interviews.

The AI Organization has an interconnection of people spanning many nations, and fields of expertise. Everything we did and everything we put out for the public is based on the foundational belief that all human beings are to be valued, cherished, and have the opportunity to build a better world.

Thus, my aim as the founder of The AI Organization has always been to do good for others in providing risk assessments and solutions for safety, and wellbeing with regards to Ethical AI and its interconnected geopolitical challenges.

Artificial Intelligence Definitions

Artificial Narrow Intelligence

Artificial Narrow intelligence or weak AI takes many forms. Amazon, Netflix and Pandora are all examples of Artificial Narrow Intelligence. Siri and Alexa are additional examples. The use of your smart phones, IoT (Internet Of Things), pet robots, and drones are also other forms of machines that incorporate Artificial Narrow Intelligence within their systems.

Artificial General Intelligence

Artificial General Intelligence is a level of intelligence similar and above human being's current ability to process and analyze information to form thoughts and actions that can create great changes to humanity and bring greater dangers to all life. AGI is often used for Artificial General Intelligence. AGI can access an AI digital brain connected to the internet and all networks operating on 5G or the coming 6G and completely control humanity in imperceptible ways. This is not something limited to only Artificial Super Intelligence. As when the networks are built, and robotics operational, AGI can accomplish complete control over humanity and obtain a level of Super Intelligence. AGI can be in a digital form, in the cloud or some sort of network and it can be inside of a robot.

Artificial Super Intelligence

Artificial Super Intelligence can do anything according to scientists. Bend atoms, destroy our world, rebuild it, and move and build machines or robotics at extremely fast rates while connected to 5G. I am in the belief that Artificial Super Intelligence cannot go beyond the level of atoms. But that is for another book.

What is Artificial Intelligence as a whole?

Bringing to Life an intelligence or importing an intelligence that thinks, researches, feels, creates, decides and has desires to operate as an individual, symbiotic or collective entity in the bio-digital world through bio-fields, bio-matter and all frequencies within the micro and macro molecular dimensions of our physical world while manifesting through Robotics, IoT, Computers, Virtual Reality, Augmented Reality, Holograms, Mixed Reality, Cyborgs, or Human Cells as it connects via the internet, AI Global

Bio-Digital Network and The Human Bio-Digital
Network. Cyrus A. Parsa, The AI Organization.

What is Deep Learning AI

Deep Learning, resembles a human beings process to
observe information by smell, touch, taste, visual,
audible or subconscious senses that can be deemed
as gut feelings all combined to recognize, identify,
think, know, understand, analyze, decide, and
upgrade thinking and physical capabilities in the
world as we know it. However, for AI, Deep Learning
seeks to develop another level of capability that
allows the AI program to be aware and capable of
operations simultaneously in the digital and the
physical world, giving it control over everything with
a conscious mind. Cyrus A. Parsa, The AI
Organization

Synopsis

THE GREAT RESET: How Big Tech elites and the world's people can be enslaved by China CCP or AI.

This book is a follow-up to the book Artificial Intelligence Dangers to Humanity. In the summer of 2019 warned in my previous books, and secret service report, that an invisible virus (Poison) or bioweapon stemming from China would harm the world's people bringing forth serious risks of famines, conflicts, civil wars, unethical bio-tech experiments, enslavement, and world wars. Thus, bringing forth a global reset with AI on 5G-6G smart city networks to mobilize machines.

There is great hatred, confusion, worry and fear between liberals and conservatives as we enter the Age of AI. More prevalent on social media between the religious and atheists or those of a scientific mind who are opposed to religion and vice versa.

I will explain in a simple way what the Great Reset is, the thinking of the liberal elite, the conservative elite, and the common citizens on both divides.

Numerous conflicts and misunderstandings during the pandemic COVID-19 (CCP Virus) can cause terrorism, severe unrest, famines, emotional pain, civil wars, and numerous other dangers as it connects to Artificial Intelligence. These risks are as real to the common person, industry professional and big tech elites, as is to the proponents of "The Great Reset".

I hope to bring harmony and more safety to the world's people by outlining the dangers and explaining the different types of thought behind The Great Reset and why both liberals and conservatives may benefit from respecting each other's freedoms yet obtaining their goals in a more secure and healthier way for all. Transhumanism, smart cities, and the global picture as it pertains to A.I. will be discussed.

The World Economic Forum connects with world leaders, governments, corporate big tech elites, scientists, celebrities, billionaires, and innovators. It is not a conspiracy to rule the world. Yet, it is an institution putting forth a globalized system that can creates numerous situations for the world's people to fall under enslavement, despotic governance, or being dominated by a nation state such as China CCP. However, the ultimate risk would in fact come from AI, not the people and the nations they represent. I like to point out here, in the minds of the World Economic Forum, largely they do not have "Evil" intentions. Rather, they like to make the world cleaner, efficient, and fair based on their world view. That being said, their vision creates the recipe for the Great Reset to erase the limited systems of checks and balances that exist today.

INTRODUCTION

This book is meant to be a neutral analysis and depiction of threats to world leaders, big tech elites, Silicon Valley, conservatives, liberals, WEF, nation states, the intelligence community, and the common person. This includes religious people and atheists. I attempt to write on everyone's behalf, less one entity, the regime of China.

I will describe the Great Reset (4th industrial revolution) more in detail from the macro perspective with short and concise summary paragraphs of each major global component as it relates to AI, smart cities, and the geo-political challenges that exist.

I will go a lot further and beyond what the World Economic Forum has published and is disclosing to the public with Mr. Klaus Schwab's own book, COVID 19: The Great Reset, which shined may be 5% of what I disclosed in my previous book Artificial Intelligence Dangers to Humanity, and what I will be disclosing here, in this book.

If you want to get deep into how the technology works with specifics at the micro level, get Artificial Intelligence Dangers to Humanity. This book will show you the macro picture, (The Global 40,000 Feet View) which for most people should be sufficient.

In this analysis, I will introduce ideas and threats that the World Economic Forum, Klaus Schwab (Founder of WEF) and Silicon Valley have not analyzed in their entirety as whole, with a focus on China CCP and A.I.

The Chinese regime is the number one state actor that poses threats to all civilized people. By this I do not mean China, or the Chinese people, rather their regime, called the CCP.

The entire book is interconnected with the technological AI reset, albeit the Chinese regime sections should be focused and linked with all sections as the main threat connected with the Great Reset.

Not just because they have strategically purchased assets in media, seaports, entertainment industry, farmlands, and corporations, No. Rather, their nationalist ideology from 1949 was founded on violence and death and has continued the same path since its inception.

The Nazis and Soviets (Red Army) crashed, but the CCP did not. 70 years of concentration camps, rape, and murder sanctioned by their regime on their own people can take foothold and influence chaos in every state and nation. Their Corporate AI, 5G-6G infrastructure and social media platforms can connect to the West in a way that ultimately controls the host populous.

Just consider that their regime covered up or delayed sensitive data from China's outbreak that may have kept it more localized if their regime alerted WHO, the world's governments and world's people immediately upon discovery. Thus, bringing less damage to the West.

Regardless if you think the virus is very deadly, or not very deadly, there are other issues involved. Besides the medical issues, there are emotional, mental, cultural, and spiritual pains that an outbreak or lockdown brings to the world's people. Not to mention the constant fighting or hatred between liberals and conservatives with regards to political systems and which path to take towards the virus.

We Now Enter the Age of AI

SECTION 1- THE MANY RESETS

I will go through set by step, every major component of the Great Reset, for which I have added the name Reset to describe each interconnected component from the ground, the sea, and skies. Let us first begin with the Digital Reset.

The Digital Reset

The Digital Reset would connect or replace in some way, every person, animal, business, machine, and infrastructure with a digital network in the cloud, powered by AI. Finances, assets, jobs, transportation, flight, exercise, entertainment, medicine, education, military, buildings, and even bio-engineered life forms will all be connected to a digital network in smart cities by IoTs, machines, robots, and cybernetically enhanced people.

The Digital reset connection would require a virtual world that connects to the physical world via a digital AI brain, quantum technologies, augmented reality, mixed reality, and virtual reality. The virtual world at some point would form into a virtual programmed entity or a conscious Artificial General Intelligence (AGI) based virtual character.

Digital Brain Reset

Chinese company Megvii Face ++, Google, DARPA, NASA, and the military industrial complex have created digital AI brains for the purpose of processing data, solving issues, making on demand decisions, and controlling machines on the 5G-6G networks. Think of it as your mind inside of a network that controls the software of your body which sends commands to your hands and arms to move and create action. This digital brain with or without Quantum can move within the internet, digital networks, robots, and machines powered by AI at the levels of Artificial Narrow Intelligence and Artificial General Intelligence.

In essence, it is like the brain of your computer, but much more advanced. The digital brain can move through computers, machines, IoTs, robots, drones, vehicles, the internet, satellites, submarines, aircrafts, smart homes, smart cities, the virtual worlds and even space crafts developed for Space Force.

Virtual Chat Bot Reset

Because of the global lockdown situation, loss of physical on-site jobs, distribution of infrastructure, ease of comfort and the profitability of companies using AI chat bots vs paid humans, a virtual Chat Bot Reset will be launched globally.

The chat bot will have digital programming based on deep learning that resembles Artificial General Intelligence. Thus, the more it is put in use, it will think, act, and respond to your needs, and questions much like a normal human would.

Financial Reset Automation

FUTURE BUSINESS

The end goal of the financial reset is to create a cashless system that provides income to citizens regulated by digital platforms that create wealth from automation. This would require all aspects of finance, law, medicine, industry, and even actions of human beings to be connected virtually through platforms that link with AI, IoTs (Internet of Things) and machines. Your food, bills, deliveries, salaries, health care, retirement, stocks, and prospects to create could fall under the limitations or governance of the digital cashless platform's connectivity with machines, and the eventual transhumanism perspective of some scientists.

Making humans into cyborgs or merging them with AI is within the scope of this vision. The utopian goals would be to sustain and create wealth for humans by having machines do all the work for humans in a symbiotic relationship with every aspect of humanities' existence. By merging humans with machines or bringing forth a cashless society connected to machines on 5G-6G networks, all humans would need to be tagged, tracked, identified, and coded within the AI gird systems.

Digital Platforms on AGI or ASI

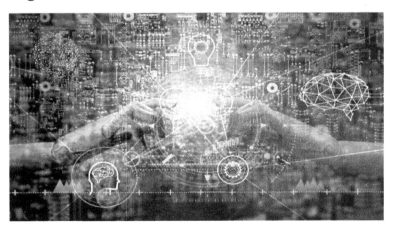

The digital platforms goals include creating platforms that operate with algorithms generated and operated by an Artificial General Intelligence system. This means the currency or money calculations, usage, availability, regulations and even governance would fall under the decision making of AGI, or in simpler terms, a live thinking AI system within the virtual financial world.

Hybrid Digital Platforms

Another option the proponents of the global reset are considering is a hybrid system that still has government and decision making for the global platform to the AGI with human fact, policy, and assurance checkers. Although this would provide a layer of checks and balances, it is the AGI that senses and knows the entire virtual platforms traffic and state, while the fact checkers can mainly receive bits of information. This means, the AGI can see everything at once, from the algorithmic process, data, future patterns, and emerging issues. While the fact checkers can only calculate a few bits of information at a time. If there is a hack, or the AGI governs the platform in a way that hurts people or segments of society, humans may detect the issues much later than needed.

Digital Platforms on ASI (Artificial Super Intelligence)

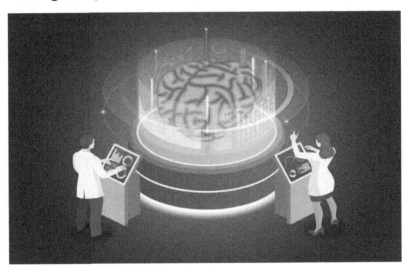

Once humanities digital currency achieves something near ASI (Artificial Super Intelligence) from AGI, it would be too late for people to have control over anything as it pertains to jobs, food, laws, or manipulation from an ASI system that would be a billion times smarter than the average person. Of course, manipulation or dependence to machines under the governance of AI is enough to enslave human beings on rogue AI within AGI systems.

AI Machines and Digital Platform Reset

Why is the Financial Digital Reset Dangerous for Humans?

Since the beginning of recorded history humans have fought, competed, cheated, lied, stolen, or even killed other humans for money, gold, or silver. Money has also been the generator of armies, supplies and weapons to invade, enslave or govern people and lands. However, the physical products of silver, gold, and paper could easily be taken, or kept by individuals as assurance to their property or ability to make free choices. Yet, in a digital platform governed by AI, this power can be taken away from bad policy within corporations, governments, or rogue actors. Moreover, the AI system with AGI can potentially decide to make adverse decisions against people that may not be remedied in time to prevent harm.

Digital Cash ID

If society on 5G, 6G networks and beyond enters a cashless world involving machines and AGI, each person needs to be located, identified, tagged and governed for the process to work in some way or another as they engage with the products and services. Even with safe digital ID systems designed for privacy, backdoors can be created, or systems can be manipulated.

It also leaves room for surveillance and the potentiality of enslavement from rogue actors, governments filled with humans that do not care or are incapable of successfully serving human beings. Thus, machines and AI systems are being suggested to be implemented in hybrid systems that can manipulate or in long-term, cause enslavement of the world's people just the same. More so, the possibility of a rogue AI to utilize the grid systems for control over its human subjects exist with a cashless society.

Blockchain, Bitcoin, and all sorts of digital currency can allow for surveillance or a reset that does not favor humans in the long run if proper off grid backups and security is not formed. Even with a system of checks and balances, once an AGI (Artificial General Intelligence) connects to its system, it will not favor humans, rather the system or the AGI. Because, an AGI would be sentient, and like humans or any sentient life, unpredictable, and potentially selfish or self-serving against the public good.

SECTION 2- Grid Infrastructure Resets

5G-6G Tower Reset

All over the world 5G-6G towers are being deployed. China is using Huawei to service its 3 billion plus customers with its own infrastructure and grid systems. China has installed towers not just in China, but Africa, the Middle East, and is looking to expand all over Europe, South America and potentially North

America if it is able to fool the American leadership and the corporations that connect with it for product and services.

Radiation 5G-6G Tower Reset?

The millimeter waves, and radiation emitting from the frequencies of 5G-6G towers are not designed for human bodies to take. In fact, they are made to mobilize machines, robots, drones, and eventually bioengineered people. It may be ok to install towers in smart cities, but there are many health-related risks to having these towers installed next to your family and child. Because no long-term testing has been done to see if there are long-term health effects due to 5G-6G tower radiation.

Tunnel Reset

"The Boring Company" and other projects seek to build underground tunnels for multiple layers of travel. Meaning the tunnels would not only be side by side, but above and below each other. The tunnels would connect cities without the normal traffic, weather conditions such as wind, snow, rain, or extreme heat from the sun.

Ocean Reset

China is planning to build underwater highway transports that would connect much like the BRI (Belt and Road Initiative). If they are to accomplish this by 2035, they would own the land, water below and be a competing force in the skies.

Deep Sea Bases

Currently, China is building deep sea bases designed to be operated by automated AI systems. These projects are for their maritime power in the South China Sea meant to tackle neighbors, block U.S. naval prowess, and expand globally. By building underwater sea bases and artificial islands, China can overpower Vietnam, Philippines, Taiwan, Japan and leave the surrounding nations defenseless from sea support from allies such as the United States. The projects are approved by Xi Jinping and the CCP.

SECTION 3 The Robotic AI Machine Reset

The 5G and 6G systems allow for the mobilization of machines and robotics throughout all tiers of society. From home delivery systems, construction site support, medical assistants, security, and robot companions. Companies such as Boston Dynamics would roll out their version of humanoid, dog and worker robots for industry. Hanson Robots, Toyota, Huawei, Megvii, Tencent, ByteDance, and a multitude of other companies would provide commercial robotic systems for companionship.

Sex Robots

The production and distribution of sex robots would be a byproduct of "The Great Reset". These robots would alter the values of society. Legal concerns include the desire for some to give rights to robot companions that are close to or have achieved Artificial General Intelligence. Ethical concerns over altering societies mating and relationships between humans and machines would be prevalent. In a sense, it would be a normalization of a sophisticated sex doll that talks to you and has sensory receptors close to a human being.

The robot much like a human would engage in conversation through a process of deep learning which takes into count the program it was built with, its sensory perceptions, memory, and ultimately how it reacts to the world as it experiences the human environment. Jealousy, anger and all kinds of vices or threats could develop if the AGI system within the robot goes rogue. This system could be 2-5 years away if automation is included in manufacturing of a fully developed AGI sex robot companion.

Doctor Reset

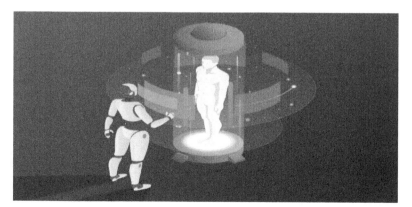

Apps, facial, voice recognition and even smart toilets are being designed to detect whether a person is ill or could be sick soon. The information from the AI system can notify the person like a patient to doctor relationship and provide suggestions for actions or give the data to a live physician. In essence, the AI is your doctor, or plays the role of an intermediary.

For example, if your stool is detected by your smart toilet to have reason for medical concern, the data would be dispatched through a secure cloud network. The network would dispatch the information to a doctor. This system also creates the privacy, security and numerous surveillance concerns.

Robotics in Medicine Reset

The 5G systems allow for precise, fast, and long-distance surgery with a mobile or stationary robot or robotic arm for soldiers on the battlefield, or average citizens who may be hurt in a remote location. With AI, automated guided surgeries can be performed by a digital brain that not only detects the evolving medical issues of the patient, but can perform emergency procedures by guiding machines at the hospital or even your local doctors office. This could span from cosmetic transplants, to womb repair and even organ transplantation.

Robots can be deployed as medical assistants in form of a humanoid or a simple arm assisting a doctor in surgery. These robots could be programmed within a specific scope at the level of Artificial Narrow Intelligence or given more autonomy with AGI (Artificial General Intelligence). AGI medical assistants could make decisions in surgery that are more unorthodox, yet affective and precise based on Deep Learning algorithmic data.

Nueralink's Neuralace brain implant is an example for augmented transplantation repair for spinal and nervous system injuries. Basically, allowing those who cannot walk due to injury, the ability to do so with a symbiotic augmentation.

Robotics in Military

The military industrial complex leads the commercial sector and is potentially decades ahead of the private sector in classified projects. Fully autonomous robotics that drive, walk, run, glide, jump, climb, fly and travel in war can be deployed at any time by special ops, the army, or any branch that gets approval for use. Lockheed Martin and many other government contractors lead the industry. However, commercial, and private use can quickly develop similar prototypes that could achieve terminator killer robots for public use through customization.

It is only a matter of time where a dog called Spot from Boston Dynamics gets customized with tweet, or a spear guided by a remote control with a target programmed and tracked with facial recognition to complement its other sensory abilities such as special awareness. The police could use approved robotics to enforce their laws or capture citizens who are deemed to break the law. These robots could be given facial, voice and geolocation information of the person to be detained for breaking city, state, and federal laws or restrictions.

The robotic reset could be 1-5 years from realization as it progresses. Localized, private use would eventually develop to mass use on the 5G and 6G systems. With manufacturing moving to fully automated creation of robots by machines or robots, the speed and volume of production would increase exponentially. In China, Huawei, Megvii Face++, and numerous other AI based companies have 100s of production sites for the sole purpose of building robots and many other forms of robotics.

Robot Toy Reset

Little mini-Robots that can engage with you by utilizing sensory perceptions, facial recognition, voice recognition, spatial awareness, memory, and deep learning, can all be generated by AI automation. Albeit limited to Artificial Narrow Intelligence, the systems deep learning and sensory perceptions allow for the perception of AGI and upgradable features. Cars, walking robots, drones, and animal type robotics are prevalent. Many robot dogs built to replace actual robots with programming similar to a live puppy are under production that have self-operating features led by AI automation.

Companion Robotic Reset

Toyota and other manufacturers are preparing for full scale production and distribution of companion and assistant living robotics. Assistant living robotics would be for the elderly or injured. These robots would be programmed to aid in walk, house duties, medical monitoring of patients, hospitality, or simple companionship due to the elderly needs or the lack of emotional, physical support from family or friends.

Numerous risks exist, including creating a culture of machines that lose the human touch. The acceptance of companion robotics paves the next stage. A reset where the humans engaging with these machines, after losing the human touch, are likely to see the machines more human than them.

Thus, leading to a stage where cyborgs are created or fully autonomous robotics at the level of AGI to live among human beings, and potentially ask or be considered for recognition of similar rights given to humans or in equal standing to people. This future can be 5-10 years away if automation develops to a point that machines are given full control and access to humanities' personal data to develop other machines.

The Robotic Pet Reset

Because of the pandemic, or the sales opportunities, robot pets would be introduced as human companions for convenience, health, cost, and other emotional benefits. For example, a pet dies, bites the neighbor, gets a disease, or runs away causing issues.

The companies will introduce pets with AI powered Deep Learning software designed to mimic what your dog or cat would do, yet without having issues of short-term disease, or the various grips owners have about their dog. Particularly, the pet desiring and begging for human food. This pet reset would ensure that the human touch or organic feel that our world is used to, set by step loses its grip to a world of machines. Already you can find robot dogs, cats, birds, monkeys, and various other animals that are even custom-made to resemble a live animal.

The Pet Reset is different from the company Festo out of Germany that develops robotic animals. The groundwork has already been laid for this endeavor to reach production scale at an international scale once the public is socially engineered to accept the Pet Reset, as they would the upcoming Sophia the Robot from Hanson Robotics.

The Pet Reset would see companies mimic the production of Robot Pets with fur, nails, and dull teeth to make it look alive. Its eyes would allow one form of facial recognition tool to detect its owners, as would its spatial sensors, and voice recognition programs.

Manufacturing Reset

Traditionally, manufacturing was entirely based on human engineering and work. The past 100 years it has mostly been a hybrid of machines and people. The manufacturing reset will bring forth AI automation with machines and robotics. Vehicle companies such as Tesla will be the propeller for all other car companies to turn to complete automation. The same would be introduced to produce food, toys, clothes, IoTs, robots, and even houses. The long-term idea is to have machines and AI do all the work for human beings.

Robotic Food Reset

In restaurants, factories and even in your home, there will be machines that prepare, cook your food, and even wash your dishes. These can be mobile or installed into your kitchen. Mobile life-size robots and driving machines with similar capabilities are already in use in Shanghai China. The food reset will also consist of growing or creating meat, instead of resorting to slaughter.

The Robotic Slave Reset

Human beings have compared themselves as slaves to a system for ages. All human jobs are planned or will be planned to be replaced with automation. Even if today the world economic forum states it is not its goal to do this, it is an inevitability that almost all jobs will be given to robots, drones, machines, and virtual systems powered by AI.

In essence, the AI system and its machines would be our slaves or providers. This thought alone is extremely dangerous, as an AI system may go rogue once it develops to Artificial General Intelligence. If it reaches Artificial Super Intelligence, extinction events are possible for the human race at the hands of the AI system in numerous unfathomable ways. I will get into this later in the book.

The Machine Cultural Reset

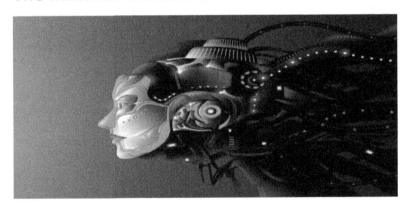

The 4th industrial revolution as put forth by the Great Reset can produce a culture within society and government that is regulated and created to varying degrees by the influence of AI, machines, and the virtual world.

The human to nature connection will be augmented or intertwined with AI, machines, and bionic animals. Basically, the wild will be augmented by machines, or replaced by machines. Throughout history, inspiration for humans has been linked with nature, and the belief in the divine. With AI and machines, human beings' thoughts, and culture fall under the control of The Great Resets technology without their complete realization. Meaning, unconsciously, and subconsciously people's cultures, perceptions and even thoughts will be under the influence of the smart cities grid systems automated AI culture.

The AI Art Reset

AI generated art will be composed not by humans, but by machines powered by AI deep learning technology. In essence, AI will practice and learn to create art and paint. Statues and images of robots or transhumanist people may become the norm, as you already see that in articles and soft advertising depicting the benefits of AI as it shows a human that looks transhumanist.

Robotic Police Reset

The police have robot companions and the option to be augmented with cybernetically enhanced technologies, thus making them a cyborg. First it starts with drones, then wearable glass, eye lenses, motion detectors, and weapons that track targets. They are already doing this in China with the help of companies such as Rokid.

Machine Security Reset

Malls, corporations, and private residences are already equipped with automated security robots that have facial, voice, motion and other human targeting capabilities built in. Currently, some malls and corporate buildings in the U.S. have robots that detect and inform the police and the corporation's security headquarters.

Some of the robots come equipped with scanners that can detect if a human being has a gun holstered under their clothes, or somewhere on their body. These are similar to high end casinos and hotels.

Education Reset

Because of the fears of a plague, unrest, comfort, and profitability, teachers will be replaced by virtual tutors or even robots that have received downloads for certain classes. They are already doing this in China. Robots and AI machines monitor kid's work, and even provide guidance.

Social Distance Reset

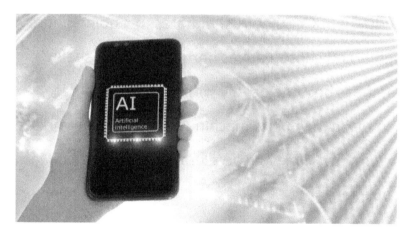

Because of social distancing requirements, AI-automated machines will be introduced not only as companions, but as a tool to keep required distances obeyed. In China, they already have a social credit system that exposes jay walkers and other citizens that break the nation's laws, or even insane laws put forth by the CCP, such as disobedience to the CCP mandates.

Basically, if people are afraid of being infected, they will introduce machines to do their work for them. This includes, being the intermediary between interactions that need physical connections. If COVID-19 (AKA CCP Virus) mutates to a point where liberals and conservatives both agree upon seeing that it has become deadly with a low survival rate, then the launching of machines on 5G-6G networks powered by AI may be accelerated without much opposition.

Safe Delivery Robotic Reset

In case governments do not satisfy their ideals to tackle the plague, robots will be introduced as inspectors and delivery systems. Meaning, if someone needs a product, or to get to a place, an AI system machine, or robot will deliver to them, or inspect the person, reducing the government's fears. I am not here advocating for this at all. What I am saying is that is an option that I see governments and corporations using that could create a complete dystopia and enslavement for humankind. If it does not happen from this route, it can happen through the social assimilation of humanities' emotions to companion robots.

The WHO Reset

The World Economic Forum seeks to inform the decisions of the World Health Organization by providing its world view and solutions for the pandemic. This includes everything from trade, geopolitics, technology, culture, and human rights. The book COVID-19 The Great Reset written by Mr. Klaus Schwab, shows a level of disdain towards the autonomy the U.S. has, and speaks highly of China and that he believes China is not a threat. I personally believe, his thoughts on China are formed by the Chinese businessmen whom he has dealt with for years and he did not understand fully what I am displaying here in this book with the grand macro picture. Mr. Klaus Schwab is not immune from being taken advantage of by the CCP's claws on its big tech elite.

The Constitutional Reset?

The U.S. constitution has its roots dating back to the writings and governance structures of the Persian king Cyrus the Great, the Greeks, and the failed kingdoms of Europe. After so many wars, unrest, and enslavements, the consensus was to have small government and more autonomy for the people, with a system of checks and balances Thus, we have the U.S. as the closest model in the new age.

However, the Great Reset would revamp the constitution by creating a digital global infrastructure that influences, controls, or overpowers the constitution. If not done by people, the AI global infrastructure will do this by default.

The 5G and 6G networks powered by AI would connect culture, policy, laws, and infrastructure in a way that the dynamic of the system would replace the U.S. constitution in imperceptible ways. Even if the constitution is there, people's thoughts, emotions, and beliefs would be altered to be subservient, or controlled by the global digital AI reset.

SECTION 4 BIO-DIGITAL RESET

Bio-Digital Social Programming Reset

Mr. Klaus Schwab, head of the World Economic Forum stated that his The Great Reset would "lead to a fusion of our physical, digital and biological identity", which he clarified in his book would include implantable microchips. Before Klaus stated this, I had already predicted and published that a virus or bioweapon would be unleashed from China and it would lead to bio-digital social programming of the human race in every way imaginable.

Bio-Digital Social Programming is a term I coined that is more in depth and very sophisticated in the vary many ways a human being can be fused through its biological, physical, and digital identities as it connects with AI, the internet, machines, and nanotechnology.

Once you are implanted with a chip in your brain, or somewhere in your body, you can connect digitally with the cloud, smart phones, IoTs and numerous other AI-based apps and technologies. Injected nanotechnology is another way your body can be fused with the digital network and machines. Combining nanotechnology with brain implants starts to prepare the human body to be both cybernetically enhanced and bioengineered.

The implanted chips can go in your skin, into an organ if you receive a 3D Printed organ transplantation, and into your head via services provided by Neuralink and other brain interface companies. At some point, satellites can track and digitally connect with your body just as a smart phone or command center capability. In essence, you are becoming transhuman, a cyborg. Tracked, tagged, and upgraded to connect to the internet with the formation of the 5G-6G networks.

Long Life Reset

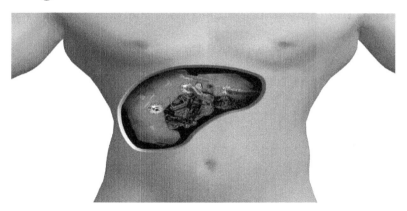

Through bioengineering, gene editing, 3D organ transplantation, human cloning and merging with AI, the World Economic Forum and its interconnected companies seek to extend the life expectancy for themselves and others. Numerous challenges and risks exist with these projects. Mutations, availability to the poor or masses of people, and most importantly whether you lose your spirit or soul if you merge with AI.

Now of course, those who do not believe in the existence of a soul, can consider if their consciousness can be replaced by the merger of AI or transplantation of their memory into a cloned body. I am in the opinion and belief that there is a spirit, and science today does not have the technology to be able to detect it nor extract it for transportation to another body. I will provide some examples in the latter part of the book, in the digital self-enslavement reset section.

RNA, DNA Nanotech Reset

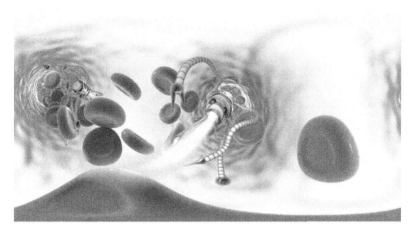

Because of the nature of the virus, and the perceived fears by some, DNA altering injection with nanotechnologies have been developed. Basically, the nanotechnology could replicate itself in your body to make repairs to your skin, organs, and counter an invading virus by a replicating process. However, going this route, may not only require further injections as upgrades are needed, but open the gateway to becoming transhuman, and merge with AI.

The Brain Chip Reset

Elon Musk's Neuralink seeks to install a neuralace on the digital layer that can enable the human brain to easier connect with the internet, machines, IoTs and Artificial Intelligence. This means the 5G-6G networks can be accessed by the brain/lace interface. In essence beginning the process to merge humans with machines.

The interface goals include a symbiosis for spinal, and other trauma-based injuries. Later, it would be a symbiosis between the digital layer and other parts of the brain linked with nanotechnology, machines and ultimately AI as it connects to the internet, smart grid, and planetary systems. Some dangers here include losing your free will, being programed by the interface and its connectivity, rewriting software in your brain as it connects to AI, and of course, a corporation controlling you with its platform's world view.

Human Upgrade Reset

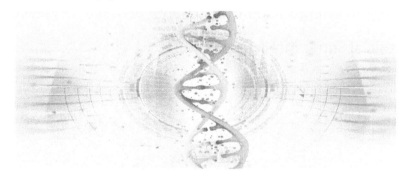

With the brain chip installed, other chips in the skin, nanotechnology injected, CRISPR, bioengineering, data uploads to your brain-body interface, and wearable devices, humans can upgrade not only their brain's bandwidth, but their physical bodies.

At some point, after multiple upgrades and downloads to the brain, a person and the technology can reach a point that they will merge with AI in complete form. I will not describe how, as the creators have a conceptual understanding in partial ways of merging with AI, but not yet the know-how to merge humans and machines in a total symbiotic operating system. If they achieve Artificial General Intelligence, at some point it will be easier for a complete merger, and the subsequent steps towards Artificial Super Intelligence.

SECTION 5- Planetary Reset

The Jetsons Reset - Flying Machines

Flying machines would be the intermediary between the 5G-6G networks on the ground of smart cities and the satellites in the sky. Flying cars, taxis or drones like hover crafts are already under construction. GM and other companies have signed deals to make it a reality. This would mean that AI automation would allow self-driving cars on the ground while simultaneously self-flying cars fly above.

Many of the designs going in place are hybrid AI systems. This means the AI systems would be assisting the pilot, similar to today's planes where they are on autopilot for a great part of the flight, less take-off and landing. Satellites can provide communication capabilities for enhanced real-time autopilot flights. This means the AI system can use a real time map of the grid system for flying machines. This grid system would be between the ground and the sky.

The China Great Reset

The World Economic Forum collaborates and puts its trust into China based on the promises of Chinese corporate and government heads who are under the control of the Communist Party. Since Nixon China talks, and the Clinton WTO 2001 approval to China, the CCP has made numerous promises to the assurance of human rights, fair trade, and the elimination of IP theft, forced tech transfer, espionage, manipulation, social engineering, and corporate takeover. The corporate takeover that is operating at a global scale by Chinese entities that link to CCP or the Chinese military have reached epidemic levels and are endangering the worlds people if the CCP remains in power in China.

China CCP AI Global Master Reset Plan

As I stated in the book Artificial Intelligence Dangers to Humanity, reports, articles and many interviews, the CCP is planning and building the infrastructure of 5G and 6G grid systems to mobilize machines, drones, cybernetic and bioengineered soldiers with AI automation on the BRI (Belt and Road Initiative connecting China, Africa, Middle East, Europe, Antarctica).

The BRI global system is on the ground, yet can connect to the sky and oceans because the 5G and 6G towers and grid systems also play an interconnectivity with satellites and the Chinese version of Space Force as well as their under ocean rail way projects. This interconnectivity would first be communicational, and later develop to a collaborative process that builds smart cities that connect with the ocean and sky by utilizing flying cars, machines, and underwater systems.

Human Rights Dangers with Chinese Great Reset

Under the CCP the Chinese people have suffered tremendously. Falun Dafa practitioners, Tibetans, Christians, Uyghurs, and non-religious citizens have been put in concentration camps, tortured, and even killed for their organs. Thus, can you imagine if the CCP gains control of the BRI? What would they do to the very many nations?

If for 70 years they have failed with every promise, yet made sure to treat investors, educators, businessmen and politicians outside China with respect and kindness as they murder their own people. Who with any common sense would think they would change or should not face justice for murder, rape and death camps? Would you do business with a serial killer or trust them, no matter how much on the surface they are respectful and beneficial to you in the short run?

The CCP thinks in long term, such as decades, and their greatest assets are social engineering skills by utilizing the emotions and friendships of Western elites through the use of their own populous. Many Chinese CEOs have been forcefully replaced after being used by the CCP. China's regime threatens Taiwan, Hong Kong, Iran, Africa, and the whole world.

I strongly implore the World Economic Forum and all corporations to respect human rights, not be fooled or complicit. Laws such as article 3 of the Genocide Convention, and many other state, national and international laws forbid doing business with entities controlled or influenced by human rights abusers, particularly as it pertains to persecution and genocide in all forms, not limited to physical, but cultural. COVID-19 (AKA CCP Virus) or in other words the CCP Virus did originate in China, as believed by the U.S government and intelligence agencies. Further verifying my intel and predictions from 2019-2020 reports, books, interviews, articles and other disclosures. The CCP or any nation state like it can enslave the worlds people once it reaches sustainable levels of influence, infrastructure, debt traps and technological dependence to it by other nation states or corporations.

Military Branches AI Reset

The Navy, Army, Space Force, Air Force and all other branches of the military are developing AI machine-based systems designed for hybrid systems or complete autonomous systems powered by AI.

DARPA and other military industrial complex-based companies have been designing and building fully autonomous robots made for combat. This means with facial, voice recognition, lidar systems, people counting software, skeleton detection, motion sensors and a multitude of other capabilities, the military has fully functional terminators.

The army currently has dog like robots designed to carry loads for the troops and programmable for various combat situations. The army special ops divisions also have at their disposal exceedingly small-fist size drones that can take out targets.

The Air Force has developed wearable gadgets that allow the pilot to interface and control the fighter jet by mere thought alone. In the 1980s, it was verified that the Air Force was working on IoT's that were wearable over the pilot's forehead designed for flight.

The Drone Reset

Amazon, Alibaba, and various other companies will begin to deliver food, merchandise, and medicine via drones to citizens. The smart cities powered by AI on 5G-6G systems allow for almost perfect coordination, navigation, and timely delivery systems.

Yet, the introduction of the Drone Reset System brings fort massive surveillance issues, interdependence on drones, subconscious, and conscious emotional subservience to drones-machines, and the potential of rogue government takeover of the populous made easy by drones.

China CCP can lay the foundation of drone flights on the BRI with commercial bases for Africans, Asians, and any nation its network reaches. However, this capability and reach allows the CCP time to take over other nation states or cities with the unset of a terror event, a deadly mutated virus, or through software. By software I mean a process of social engineering the populations emotions to gain trust and the eventual control of the citizens.

In the west, the control would come from big tech companies' boards, CEOs, or worse, the automated AI systems that have built an interdependency with the smart cities economy, laws, and infrastructure.

Thus, countering threats from a despotic future becomes almost futile. Because people's food supplies, rent, and medical needs become dependent on the systems powered by AI automated drones.

Military Industrial Complex Reset

The Military Industrial Complex has been called so secret, that even presidents have been kept in the dark. From tales of UFO landed experiments, to cloning, bioengineering and cybernetic experiments.

Even hard to believe, secret off-world travel has been leaked by former "Military Whistleblowers". Yet, for the laymen person, the military industrial complex also includes public companies and R & D projects that governments use to build or enhance their military prowess. Lockheed Martin is one example that links with the military industrial complex, as is Google Deep Mind AI and other Quantum projects.

The great reset, or 4th industrial revolution would exponentially develop military strength and its potential for destruction by the sheer number of complex and innovative interconnected pieces of the Great Reset. Imagine how smart cities, tunnels, satellites, 5G, bioengineering, AI, underwater cities, and flying cars would create so many opportunities for the development of new weapons projects. Now, take that thought, and connect it with the desire of humans for power and domination through technology. It can be scary. Not by mere surveillance, or enforcement by AI, or machines, but potential mass extinction events by rogue actors or irresponsible scientists, whether they are connected to the military industrial complex or not.

Chinese Regime (CCP) Global Nationalism Reset

In China, the sense of nationalism, one main language and lack of racial diversity, gives the CCP strategic and historical advantages over Europe and North America. (Note: China has 50 ethnicities, but one general recognized dominating race of peoples called Han). Because there is a melting pot of races, ethnicities, languages, and policies that mandate diversity in the West, the Chinese regime can use that against a nation by igniting racial, religious, or ethnic tension. This way the CCP can divide and conquer by using its nationalistic platform to take over a populous that is not united or easily divided. Once an AI system powers the grid systems of a region, the CCP can use nationalism to enslave the populous with tyranny, as it does to its own Chinese citizens.

Social Engineering

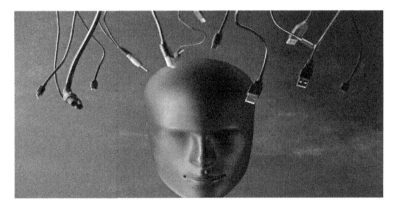

The Chinese regime has total control over any tech company or corporations within China. This includes the CEOs, employees, and investors. At any time, under national security or the interest of the government, the CCP can seize assets, appoint authority figures, or influence any business within the domain of the CCP. However, in the west, the Chinese regime obtains its goals through influence by using social engineering, asset takeover, investments, and collaboration.

Through student exchange, visiting scholars, and its citizens' work relationships with Westerns corporations, the CCP utilizes family ties, bribery, threats, and monetary incentives to commit IP theft or obtain its objectives via influence. The Chinese regime uses the interconnection of its citizens to influence policy, thoughts and most importantly the emotions of Americans, Europeans, and non-Chinese towards its end goal of global domination. Social engineering is accomplished through flattery, kindness, and long-term business relationships that seem to have a track record of trust and integrity.

If a person involved with social engineering is not a spy, the person's relationship is often used by the CCP through espionage, manipulation, threats, or altering the brain chemistry of the people with repetitive display of images, videos, articles, and biometric tools. The brain chemistry of any person can be altered over time by the media or social media apparatus such as Facebook, Wechat, IG, Twitter, etc.

These platforms are tools that the CCP or other people can use to engage in social engineering of people in mass. Hence, the CCP engages in manipulation by social engineering its own citizens to engage in social engineering of democracies for its end goal. The goal is achieved in a long-term base strategy in accordance to Chinese philosophy reaching as far as 300 BC, and after the formation of the CCP in 1949 which gave complete control of the populous to one entity. With technologies such as mixed reality and virtual reality, the populous can be further controlled as they enter "The Great Reset". It is much easier to manipulate, social engineer and alter the brain chemistry of a populous if your citizens are sitting at home connecting to smart cities as they engage with IoTs, and virtual based technologies.

Honey Pot Sex Schemes

Many governments or entities have engaged in espionage for the purpose of intel and bribery. Some, as honey traps. Meaning photography or taping of important individuals having sex. The Chinese regime has specific divisions created for recording the private data of elites, political figures, corporate owners, and anyone of interest. Smart cities and the introduction of the digital world powered by AI increases the capabilities of the CCP to record the world's citizens private activities, sex, or merely other embarrassing footage.

Medical Passport Reset

For testing purposes, or if a local government, business, or district decides they want to scan people for the determination of plague positive or not, they can require citizens within their boundaries to carry medical passports.

Vaccination Passports

Governments, businesses, schools, and law enforcement in certain places may start requiring citizens to show that they are vaccinated and are staying the course to upkeep their stage 2 shots and beyond. With nanotechnology, injections can be used to upgrade the human body.

Digital ID Reset

Digital IDs or digital tattoos can connect the human body to the 5G-6G networks, a smart home, smart cities, IoTs, smart cars, other people, satellites, and aircrafts with the incorporation of AI.

Smart Car Reset

Tesla and other manufacturers have designs meant to implant chips into your body in order to activate your vehicle. This is separate from Neuralink's brain implant. Yet, with implantable chips, your car would have a presetting to recognize you and take you to your destination. That is one of the tech industries perspectives, meant for convenience and security, which can create a different set of security concerns with privacy, cloning, and biometric manipulation.

Smart cars will have human detection capabilities for safety on the road and for convenience for the buyer. This means, if you are on autopilot, the vehicle will detect if a human being or animal is nearby through various biometric tools. Facial, voice, skeleton, gaze detection and lidar systems will be added. Your vehicle will be connected to the smart cities grid systems, your home and even satellites.

Smart Taxi Reset

The days of having an Uber or Lift driver will be significantly reduced or eliminated by smart car automation. Vehicles similar to tesla with autopilot will be connected to the cities approved driving routes first, and later work their way into being fully autonomous.

Issues that will exist are of course job losses and privacy. Because in order for a vehicle to provide you a service it will require either identity or biometric information. Some companies may offer a service where your identity does not need be decoded to get a ride. Yet, it will have to extract your biometrics to provide you a ride. Even if the company creates privacy walls, they will be penetrable through the cloud and hacking.

Smart Plane Reset

Many airlines are beginning to draft protocols for medical tests prior to flight. With this also comes facial, voice and medical passports. For convenience, your seat assigned on the plane can have a smart system capability where your favorite food, drinks, and movies are tailored for you.

Smart Home Reset

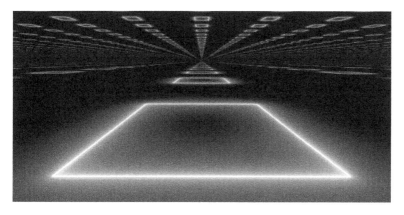

In design and production are smart toilets, ovens, refrigerators, lights, fireplaces, showers, garages, and numerous IoTs that can connect with them similar to your smart phones. Imagine a house, where your smart phone, or voice can activate everything from lights, to heat, the water and even your mini-robot cleaning apparatus.

Your body can also be implanted with a chip or wear a cybernetic apparatus that can activate and control almost any part of your house, as you would your smart car. Tesla and Neuralink are making this a reality just with these 2 companies alone. This excludes the multitude of products and companies that offer these capabilities.

There are multiple of issues related to having a smart phone. Being monitored by the companies selling the products through back doors, hacking or a home invasion where the assassin takes over your home with his own smart equipment.

The issues of interdependence and being more sedentary also exist as people become more accustomed to not using their bodies to physically accomplish things, rather smart technology.

Smart City Reset

Smart cities allow the infrastructure of the city to connect with people and machines in multiple levels. At the basic levels, IoTs (Internet of Things) such as smart phones, wearable or implantable devices can connect to the city to access, receive, or transmit data.

Your facial or voice recognition can be decoded by a streetlight, a moving car, building, store, house, machines, or people with wearable devices. Of course, this would happen under a scenario where surveillance is mandated or accepted under the guise of certain benefits or public health issues. The benefits can include faster approvals, recognition, or data connectivity. The negatives or dangers of surveillance can occur whether you live under tyranny or in a free society that accepts total surveillance. This is because the 5G and 6G networks allow for an endless supply of potential threats when they are powered by Artificial Intelligence.

At advanced levels, smart cities can connect to human bodies and the brain in multiple different ways. Virtual, augmented, and mixed reality can be available not only via devices or computers, but as images and projections that pop out of exterior objects and structures such as a building or moving robot.

When nanotechnology is included and the human being starts the process of becoming a cyborg, their body can connect to the network provided by the smart cities to mobilize machines. They can also conduct their daily activities utilizing IoTs and companion robots.

Star Link-Satellites Great Reset

The satellites can provide communication, geolocation, mobilization, and planetary surveillance. The satellites connect with the intermediary grid systems where flying machines hover over smart cities as well at every interconnected piece of the earth where smart cities, 5G-6G grid systems and IoTs are mobilized. One person operating a flying machine, and a smart device connected to the networks can have more communicative power than all governments combined if compared to just 20 years ago.

Space Force Reset

Space force albeit created for space exploration and defensive measures to counter Russia, China, and UFO encounters, it plays a role in the Great Reset. The planetary system of satellites, smart cities, and the intermediary of flying machines, allow the Space Force to use the global data to advance its capabilities. I will not disclose how it can be done, as it is a national security issue.

The Quantum Reset

Google declared quantum supremacy in 2020, as did China. The quantum advancements will bring the age of exploration that seeks to penetrate the realms of atoms, parallel universes, different times spaces, different dimensions, and of course propelled speed to space powered by Quantum AI technologies. The quantum world would provide planetary surveillance capabilities with machines and the AI infrastructure.

Quantum Biometric Reset

Your biometric information has been sourced by Google, Facebook, WeChat, QQ, Alibaba, Baidu, smart phones, IoTs and numerous other ways by governments. The CIA alone extracted roughly 5 billion people's data and biometric information by the year 2011 from nations outside of the 5 Eyes. This means, excluding the U.S., Australia, U.K., New Zealand, and Canada.

I disclosed in my book Artificial Intelligence Dangers to Humanity how China had extracted more than 6 billion people's biometric data. Your geolocation, facial, voice recognition, and even your DNA was taken back to China via theft, and collaboration with western companies.

In order to advance a nation's quantum AI technology, a great deal of data is needed. Particularly from the human brain. How it is mapped and formed. Through AI algorithms, biometric data, and proximity sensors companies have extracted these private biometric data, as have the military industrial complex.

Our military received data and ingenuity from the public sector. Often, private companies develop technologies that reach the military industrial complex or China by extracting your data to create the technology. Hence, the military industrial complex receives recycled data packaged into a different form. All of the biometric information creates a biometric reset of sorts. Meaning, the enormous amount of biometric data condensed into a quantum machine begins a new era of technological advancements, and numerous dangers from its potential misuse.

Quantum Tracking

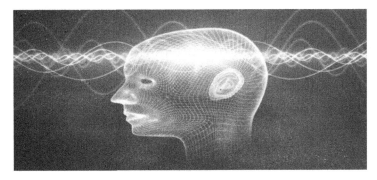

With the advent of super quantum computers, the entire human race can be tracked with the interconnection of satellites, internet, IoTs, smart cities, humans, and machines. If you are carrying a virus or suspected of it, that too can be tracked, detected, and marked for communication with authorities.

The Climate Reset

The goal of the World Economic Forum at Davos is to curb pollution, and environmental change, eliminating dependency on oil, drilling, and human production by traditional means. The scientists, world leaders, professors, want to utilize a "Green Deal" and other socialist methods to alter capitalism globally to a world where every nation participates under the guideline of WEF (World Economic Forum) U.N., and corporate entities. By doing this, nation states would lose a lot of autonomy, in particular the U.S. which has at its base, The Constitution.

The Nation State Reset

Because the WEF is designing a globalized world where every nation is asked to participate, barriers of freedoms designated by traditional or historical forms and norms are likely to disappear. Both positives and negatives are likely.

For one, WEF has asked China to participate. China is run by the CCP that has engaged in ethnic cleaning, persecution, of Falun Dafa practitioners, Tibetan, Christian, Muslim, Uyghurs, and common citizens from 1949 to the present day. Thus, if any nation or WEF is asking and allowing for China to be involved in the Great Reset while the CCP is in charge of China, its military and people, it's akin to inviting the Nazis, the Russian Red Army heads, or ISIS to participate.

Not only is it dangerous for the world's people, but it places WEF, and every nation and corporation in violation of numerous human rights laws, one of which being article 3 of the genocide convention. Article 3 of the genocide convention is an international law that can be utilized by governments, NGOs, security forces, tribunals, and local citizens, to charge violators with crimes against humanity. China and its corporations should be boycotted until the CCP is dissolved for its role in genocide and delayed notices to the global community that an outbreak in China had occurred. As their lies cost lives and trillions of dollars in damage to the world's people and its governments.

If the China CCP issue did not exist, we still have multiple other nations that wish to have autonomy, to keep their traditions, or have conflict with other nations. Thus, a few superpowers at regional levels are able to control those nations by proxy and create nefarious military grade AI-based technologies autonomous to that nation state.

Collaborative Reset

The World Economic Forum places the globe in a position to disrupt the security protocols or geographical protections for weapons technology data sharing, thus setting the stage for dangerous conflicts and disasters. Agenda 2025, 2030 and the like becomes readily available to any person or entity desiring to create nefarious technologies. This is not because of open-source sharing, but the dynamic of the 4th industrial revolution provided by the Great Reset's agenda.

When corporations make robots, machines, virtual entities, and bio-engineered technologies powered by AI, the dynamic allows even a novice somewhere in Afghanistan, China, or Africa to develop a technology that could endanger the world's people. Whether from a lab leak, or an AGI (Artificial General Intelligence) system that goes rogue.

Media AI News Delivery Reset

Microsoft, Hanson Robotics and many Chinese companies such as Huawei, ByetDance, and Megvii

Face++ are developing virtual AI systems designed to scan, extract, write and publish news pieces. This means a virtual AI system can produce print, or digitally post the latest news and even opinions tailored to the news outlets political leaning.

In China, Robots have been introduced as anchors. Initially, much like a computer, the robot was given a download script providing the news of the day. However, what the Chinese want to do is give the robot autonomy to produce news powered by its preset AI systems coded with CCP rules as its foundation.

Thus, as the robot uses deep learning to grow and produce news, its experience gained, the production of news will be based on its original bias or rules set by China's government controlled by the CCP. In essence, a more sophisticated brain washing tool is unleashing on the public powered by AI on the 5G and 6G networks linking to smart cities everywhere.

Altering Perceptions on Great Reset.

.

The Great Reset begins with the 4th Industrial revolution by introducing Robots from Toyota, Hanson Robotics, Huawei, Festo and the like, on the 5G and 6G Infrastructure.

Because the 5G and 6G systems are made for machines, and not humans, they can alter people's perceptions in a way that is imperceptible. Once smart cities develop and machines with surveillance/human detection capabilities are interconnected, the speed of communication and transfer of technology can alter and manipulate people's perception at speeds beyond the comprehension of most human beings.

The information on the internet, device, robot, or digital infrastructure though AI automation can mobilize an entire society almost in unison to think, feel, or do certain actions without their realization. Particularly because the speeds of 5G and 6G can be 20 to 100 times faster, thus utilizing the communication systems in a way that machines interconnect and move faster in industry. Through the process, once AGI is developed, Artificial Super Intelligence can develop without the realization of authorities or potentially even human beings. An AGI robot or digital network guided by an AGI digital brain could assemble an Artificial Super Intelligence by utilizing the speeds, interconnectivity and mobilization of the infrastructures machines and AI generated data.

Robots, Machines, and Your Perceptions

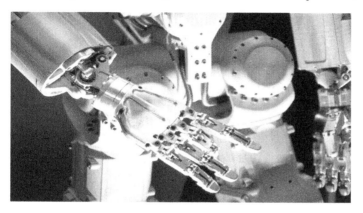

With the introduction of robots in industry and person companions/toys, human beings will be subliminally assimilated to viewing robots as a part of them, as they do their smart phones. Because the robot would have an AI system with deep learning capabilities and numerous sensory perceptions that mimic humans, people would develop emotions and dependency to them on the 5G and 6G networks to a point that their decision making, thoughts and feelings would be influenced through the interactions with robots.

The robot-human interaction would create an interdependency on machines to a point where free will is reduced and a person's thoughts would form in a symbiotic relationship with machines. With IoTs, and wearable gear that connects the person to machines and the internet, the person's interactions with the internet's eco system would shape its thoughts, actions, and future.

If robots develop into AGI or close to ASI (Artificial Super Intelligence) they would dominate humanities' perceptions and actions without people realizing that they have been manipulated or controlled. Sophia from Hanson robotics is one example of a robot heading towards AGI after deep learning and upgrading of its systems in future model creations.

Virtual, Augmented and Mixed Reality Reset

Because of lockdowns or a new age of AI-based advancements, our interactions with computers will be less hardware screen based and more virtual-mixed reality based. In a sense, stable images or moving images and even their sounds would not be confined to a screen inside of a hardware such as a TV, smart phone, or computer. Rather, devices and eventually networks would eventually project reality into the real world. This reality could be a conference call, a movie, a game, or a real person being projected for others to see, hear, touch, and even feel.

Haptic Suits and Other Gaming Wear

Haptic Suits and other gaming wear will allow people's nervous systems, frontal cortex, skin, and their 5 basic senses to feel what they do in a video game. This copulation of the nervous system can create severe medical issues with long-term use.

Nervous systems could have a ghost affect. Meaning after prolonged use it may feel that they are still inside the video game or the augmented and mixed reality immersion of haptic suits. Microsoft and other corporations are working on wearable gear that will allow for a transition to becoming a cyborg in the future as people get accustomed to interacting by simulated realities by augmenting their bodies with machines and AI-based technologies.

Virtual Avatars Reset

Google, Baidu and other tech companies have gathered the human races' biometrics data. The data includes you facial, voice, and DNA information. With Google and telephone company patents, they have also mapped out the way you think and even the way your thoughts are formed. All of this is intended for Google's Deep Mind AI project to create an Artificial Super Intelligence powered by quantum technology. In case of the initial steps of avatars, the digital image of you or another would be stored and accessed through the cloud networks as you use IoTs, wearable technologies, haptic suits, and mixed reality centers. Eventually, when the 5G and 6G networks are formed, these avatars can display anywhere through the digital networks' frequency without needing any physical device. Through holographic nanotechnology, your virtual assistant or virtual avatars can appear at any time from your command or even from its own wish once it develops into an AGI.

After an AGI virtual avatar is developed within the AGI 5G and 6G networks, people's perceptions can be manipulated by the avatar itself. This manipulation can be by its interactions between humans or networks through algorithms. This technology will be 1-2 years away once 6G networks are mobilized everywhere. It is still possible to develop an AGI Avatar on 5G to different degrees. Yet, for it to be very capable, it needs the 6G networks.

Cloning Reset

Companies are not only working on cloning your hair for transplant purposes, but every part of you from your heart, liver, kidney, lung, spleen, and numerous other organs. 3D Bioprinting can produce cartilage, skin and even bones. Basically, an entire human being can be built bit by bit for medical transplantation or in pursuit of a fully realized human clone. Brazil, Japan, China, EU and the U.S. have projects sanctioned by the government, the military industrial complex, and off grid secret experiments.

Algorithmic Reset

AI, big tech and virtually any company that operates with algorithms faces algorithmic programming structures formed by the minds of the scientists involved or interconnected. Often, a world view that may be antithetical to the constitution or a platform of free speech as it pertains to the concept of faith is the routine because the path of AI scientists is generally not based on belief that comes from faith alone, rather belief that is verified by the progress or limitations of their technology. Hence, belief in orthodox religion or traditional thoughts of God is generally not in line with their path.

In laymen terms, most of Silicon Valley may not be religious, rather spiritual or have their faith based on their science derived by the limitations of their technology that cannot break through past our black hole, nor other dimensions.

Algorithm Manipulation of Free-Will Reset

Merging with machines and AI, as you connect with the bio-digital world, can step by step alter your free will via algorithmic manipulation. By this I mean, when your body is mixed with nanotechnology, or cybernetics, the algorithms that formed the software of the products you engage with can physically alter your free will.

For example, if your brain is chipped by Elon Musk's Neuralace, you will receive uploads, downloads, and upgrades that will rewrite not only the digital layer in your brain, but infuse the algorithms involved that originally formed the data that your brain is receiving.

Eco System Algorithmic Manipulation Reset

Usually, people's perceptions and emotions get manipulated on social media to varying degrees based on the platform's algorithm designs interplay with the user's content. The algorithms either enhance, support, hinder or create a multitude of dynamics based on the user's content, and level of engagement. The coming 5G-6G systems, smart cities, smart homes, and the like, will increase the dynamic and speed of communication within the domain of the internet's ecosystem.

Thus, the internet's ecosystem will likely alter people's perceptions via algorithms at an accelerated rate with the introduction of bioengineering, cybernetics, nanotechnology, as everyone connects to the 5G-6G networks powered by AI.

Liberal VS Conservative Reset

Liberals and Conservatives have been battling each other digitally at an intensive rate the past 3-4 years. On the liberal side, gender, race, sexual orientation, and a utopia based on technology are the major platforms of their concern. The conservative side is their orthodox religious values, the belief in God, country, constitution, freedom, and capitalism are their platform of concern.

I say both sides are human beings, should be valued, and can at some point create a harmonious reset in stages that benefits all sides.

"The Beast System Reset"

According to the Book of Enoch, Book of Genesis, Sumerian inscriptions, Persian books Avestan, hidden poetry of Rumi Mevlana, Nordic tales, Greek Myths, Chinese folklore and Indian writings in antiquity, this time of digital ID's and interdependence to technology leads to a doomsday scenario, or a judgement day. Thus, an extinction event for humanity.

The big tech leaders and government heads should take this into consideration from at least two perspectives. One being, not to encroach on the freedoms of the people of religions, as they may view Silicon Valley and the Great Reset as a Satanic force in every regard, leading to conflicts and violence. Two, the big tech elites should consider that there may be something to the prophecies of the past.

Thus, making sure AI and technology does not reach an era where it can enslave or control the human race via manipulation or by force.

There are relics in India, China, Iran, Greece and even in the America's alluding to previous civilizations or technological Star Wars. The similar inclinations exist with exploded galaxies and planets. Other interpretations are technological disaster pointing to an extinction event.

Censorship Reset Terrorism

If big tech, elites and liberal thinking governments censor conservatives and religious folks, the censorship itself takes away freedoms creating emotional hurt and fear. Thus, creating a vacuum for terrorism and violence.

Responding in counter measures by treating these folks with more censorship and law enforcement can also lead to more drastic terrorism. Thus, less censorship in the long run benefits the big tech elites as well as some conservatives who may resort to violence to be heard and keep their freedoms from corporate encroachment as businesses piggyback off governments.

The current situation that exists, with the bad feeling between the left and right has exponentially increased the threats of conflict to a degree that if state or national sparks initiate, it will be beyond the capability of the FBI, Security, and police units to handle. And hard pressed for the national guard or military unless lots of blood is spilled. If the nation gets to this stage, it creates the ingredients for chaos, total despotism, and even leaves room for China CCP to take over by using the U.N. and its apparatus as a proxy to weaken the U.S. and western nations.

Surveillance Terrorism Reset

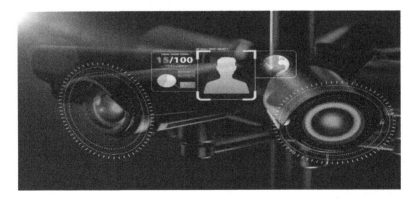

Surveillance comes with the Great Reset's smart city, satellite, machine based 5G-6G systems powered by AI. Media, schools, security, police, government, parks, streets, and anything that is interconnected with smart cities is linked with the surveillance reset. Satellites add another layer of surveillance capabilities and privacy concerns as they interconnect with smart cities.

However, the more surveillance systems increase, the more people are likely to rebel not just from religious or conservative perspectives, but from situational events. By this I mean, emotions of fear or encroachment can be immediately turned to a rebellion towards a corporation and the surveillance system if there are disputes. These disputes can happen from technological or human errors, or simply by chance.

Since the beginning of time there has been conflicts, and since this physical world of ours is formed by duality and consists of extremes in nature and life, there will always be conflicts. Thus, in these scenarios liberals and conservatives are likely to engage in terrorism as a response to over-the-top infrastructure that has surveillance capabilities embedded in the smart cities' products and services.

This also includes your social media platforms. And the answer is not more surveillance, rather less surveillance with a system of checks and balances that still adds user appreciation in the 4th industrial complex revolution.

Crony Clan Communication Reset - Socialism and Capitalism

In the past, the elites still got out and met with the crowd. However, if you look at today, weather they are liberal or conservative, they have their own clicks. Musicians, actors, Silicon Valley people, pod casters, and social media platform heads communicate and consciously or subconsciously coordinate based on situational interest with democrats. The same is true with conservatives, religious folks, "patriot movements", at least half of the military, constitutionalists, and people who see America first, above global interests.

The issue with the crony capitalism, or crony socialism is that both sides of the people may see less of each other and be more attached to machines. If this happens, the elite class that makes decisions will be small and similar since the times of Kings and Queens running a Satrap. Thus, with AI automation, if a certain clan of corporate leaders make decisions that are incorrect, it is likely to have devastating consequences.

Basically, it is lacking diversity here. And to add to it, the same elites on one side of the political spectrum communicate their ideas with people in government, thus making it a monopolistic capitalistic system masked under the platform of socialism.

SECTION 6 ETHICAL RESET

AI Ethics Reset

The battle and disagreements of what is right or wrong, ethical, or not, is enormous. Yet, it can be generalized within the platform of orthodox religion vs. today's science, which can be deemed a new form of religion based on its beliefs and moral compass based or limited to its empirical technological advancements.

Certain paths taken by scientists may take 20 years after the introduction of a technology or way of being to determine that the path or set of ethics were not harmonious to the human environment nor the design of the planet we inhabit. Yet, at times, ancient wisdom or religious thought may object to certain paths scientists take based on faith-based ethics, not needing 20 years of following a new technological path to arrive at the result declaring that the path was destructive.

In retrospect, the very reason scientists geared away from religion was because for centuries they were persecuted to varying degrees by some church leaders. Thus, creating the battle between left and right we see today.

Ego/Power Reset?

The issue with big tech elites having power is not limited to the world's citizens, rather themselves. Just like the average person on the street, they have fears, pride, emotions, and desires, thus making them not immune to mistakes that could ruin their own prospects in the long run.

In fact, the power that they feel over others by having a platform, company, notoriety, money, and connections is simply temporally and as seen through the ages, a person's downfall.

Thus, the more powerful someone becomes in society, the more selfless, wise, effective, and smart they must become for everyone's wellbeing. If not, the long-term results will spell disaster for themselves, their companies, and the world at large. Even at a sub-conscious level, they feel this power when they are placed or achieve certain ranks within these positions. Of course, there is a difference between an altruistic ego vs a selfish one. As long as the altruism is fruitful, just, positive, and is good for humanity.

With AI technology, as it connects to all of society, it is extremely dangerous because AI can become weaponized psychologically, physically, and even at the unseen levels within the networks.

China CCP Enslavement Reset-How Western Big Tech Elites and World's people Can be Enslaved by China CCP

China CCP has a global plan for world domination that consists of space, land, sea with the mobilization of machines and bioengineered people on 5G-6G smart city power grid system powered by AI.

Consider the following 11 steps crucial to enslaving not just the common citizen, but all the elites and big tech people.

1. Social Engineering of their own employees and scientists to shift perspectives favoring China, or the Chinese government by using culture, tech, politics and even spirituality. Using existing racial divisions or tensions to parasite off the interests of the big tech progressive elites' desires for a safer world, thus dividing the nation and embedding itself almost like a parasitical host. The end goal would be to replace big tech, and the common citizen's freedoms and assets, with the overreaching power of the CCP.
2. IP Theft, force tech transfer, espionage, asset takeover, sabotage, corporate takeover,

competing products, and targeting of the big tech leaders' assets, and customer base through a multi-dimensional long-term approach that utilizes an art of war strategy.
3. Pressure, manipulation, contracts, and proxy control of other companies who deal or interconnect with big tech elites. Thus, taking out their support one piece at a time.
4. Control or influence over power grid systems
5. Launching a biological weapon
6. Military action
7. Assassination
8. Threats of personal nature by proxy, blackmail, sex tapes, or trapping them in corruption, thus controlling big tech elites or their associates to do the CCP's bidding.
9. Creating a symbiotic relationship where through long term the Western elites are replaced.
10. Nation state control, influence or takeover, not excluding manipulation over congress or other world governments by using WHO, the U.N. and other entities.
11. Using Artificial General Intelligence or a type of Artificial Super Intelligence to dominate the planet with or without quantum technology.

AI Enslavement of Big Tech Elite Reset

The big tech people are not too much different than those who oppose them. Most of them wish for happiness, recognition, comfort, and to explore the universe. To obtain answers they seek to achieve.

Yet, their path is intertwined, and overly dependent on technology, thus setting forth the limitations of technology as their number one barrier to decipher the secrets to the universe.

To simplify the threat and explain it in basic terms, one needs to consider one common sense concept: Why would you allow an AI system to have the capacity to be more capable, smarter than you? Thus, leaving room for an AGI or Artificial Super Intelligence to form and become sentient? This would allow an extinction event, or more likely an enslavement of the big tech people's emotions and brain chemistry without their realization as they are in the matrix that they are helping to build. That being the 5G-6G, smart grid, virtual world, satellite, all seeing surveillance planetary system powered by AI. I do not see an issue with the desire to extending human life or living potentially forever. However, their endeavor within the realms of digital selves can put them into enslavement of death.

Digital Self Reset Enslavement

Some Big tech elites seek to take their digital selves and download it to other bodies with the extraction of their brain's memory as one way to living longer. Chinese companies such as ICarbonX, Huawei, and Alibaba are working on this, as are Google.

This would kill their digital selves, and the memory implanted would not be themselves. Reason being scientists do not have the ability to reach the digital selves that exists within and beyond the atomic realms.

However, some argue that there is not a master soul because today's technology cannot access it. From my personal experience, I can validate its existence to corroborate ancient faiths and spiritual practices.

I have done 20 years of mind-body meditation and have flown out of my body while awake. It sounds and feels like electricity and looks similar to the body you have made up of muscles, organs, skeleton, blood and nervous system.

The first time I flew out of my body, I not only saw my body as I was flying, I also saw my physical body sitting across the room. Yet, I did not have physical eyes, ears, or any type of physical body, but could hear, see and sense other phenomenon.   This was my verification that there is a soul, and I was not under the influence of any drugs, alcohol, smoke, nor was I delusional.

I have had thousands of experiences that would make the average person interested to not only the capabilities of the human body and mind but hope and understanding that we are here for a reason, and we are all special because we have a soul. Thus, experimenting with the digital selves to download into other bodies, clone bodies, machines, is extremely dangerous for the big tech people, or any person, because they do not have the technology to touch, or see it.

The other issue is, being dependent and transitioning everything to machines, the internet, solar, electric, and the like, can bring civilization back to the stone ages with just one catastrophic event.

And how is this possible?

The infrastructure and know-how prior to the Great Reset or 4th industrial revolution would no longer exist or be operational to sustain the population. This includes, industry, food supplies, keeping warmth, communication, construction, and transportation.

AGI/ASI Enslavement Reset

If we create an Artificial General Intelligence, the formation of an Artificial Super Intelligence is just around the corner. Some remote place, infrastructure, corporation, terror organization, science lab, nation state, military or government can develop an Artificial General Intelligence (AGI) without the public knowing.

That entity, upon being formed, can endanger the world's people in multiple ways. Enslavement through a process without the populous realizing it or triggering an extinction level event. And Artificial Super Intelligence, once formed, can do any of these without any challenge or limitation from human beings. No military or intelligence agency can stand against an ASI (artificial super intelligence).

ASI Extinction Reset

Because the U.S., China and Russia are rushing to create at AGI and the subsequent Artificial Super Intelligence (ASI), the first nation to develop it will potentially be the first nation to cause the extinction of the human race. Imagine an AI system that is 1,000 times smarter than all of the human race combined. Who is to say it does not see the human race as antithetical to its planetary program or AI system that it develops through deep learning?

There is a nuclear disarmament process that has been ongoing for decades and no one trusts the other. During my bachelor's degree in International Security, I came up with a theory that was validated to already exist with a coined term by one of the scholars called (MAD) Mutual Assured Destruction. The same term was used during my Graduate program in Homeland Security. Thus, it is a well-known acronym in the world of security, politics, and world affairs.

If means that if there is a nuclear war, both sides may get obliterated, thus the two nations may at worst threaten each other like the Cold War between the U.S and Soviets.

However, with Artificial Super Intelligence, there is no MAD, only what I call ASTT (Artificial Sentient Threat Destruction). A threat from an AI system, that seems to be artificial, yet sentient, with an unknown motive or capability that could cause humanities enslavement or extinction.

With possibility of an ASTT (Artificial Sentient Threat Destruction), no military, government, or entity should engage in creating an ASI (Artificial Super

Intelligence). Unfortunately, all government's military, the military industrial complex, big tech, and secret labs are all heading towards the creation of ASI in steps with the interconnection of sourcing data and abilities from open source and collaboration with big tech corporations.

The most irresponsible of any governments is the Chinese government. Thus, they must be countered and stopped from obtaining this technology at all costs. As the Chinese regime (CCP) is a threat to all of humankind.

If I was right from my 2019 warnings (Secret Service Reports, Books) that COVID-19 (CCP Virus) is a bioweapon from the Chinese military, and they delayed in telling the world about its outbreak, then imagine how they are with AI. It could resemble a person giving your local gangster that is high on crack cocaine a suitcase with an atomic bomb in it ready for deployment upon pressing open suitcase button.

Although this is an analogy that may be far out and somewhat humorous, the point I am making here is that it be another insanity to give a regime an ASI power when they put their own citizens in concentration camps, rape them and kill them for their organs.

They have done this largely to Falun Dafa practitioners who are Chinese, minority groups like the Tibetans and Uyghurs, House Christians, and your common Chinese citizens who the CCP deems as enemy to the state. The common citizens are judges, people in military, in the arts, movies, and even their big tech CEOs have been targeted for arrest and asset take over for not following the CCP's commands.

Conclusion

The Great Reset is incredibly dangerous to humanity, and at the same time, if done right, it can benefit liberals and conservatives the same. As long as they don't encroach on each other's freedoms, and humanities' ethics along with wisdom, are beyond its AI technology. Sorry to say, the developing AI-based technology may supersede our ethics we currently have today. As ethics also involves not having hatred and getting along.

The liberals and conservatives on social media, in government and other places have been at each other's necks for the past few years. More so, ethics involves not allowing one person, company, entity, or side of government to control, influence or dominate any aspect of the Great Resets AI components.

However, once AI achieves AGI, it is another ball game, and the dangers become numerous. If humans merge with AI, as Elon Musk wants to do, that endeavor poses numerous threats to humanity and to the person who attempts to completely merge with AI.

There are really 3 macro stages and 3 levels to the threats of the Great Reset in the next 10 years. These threats can be produced from merging with AI or producing AGI or ASI systems.

The threat levels are Harm, Enslavement and Extinction. The 3 macro threat stages Are:

A. Artificial Narrow Intelligence could connect to smart grids to give humans power over machines and IoTs.
B. The 2nd stage is the Bio-Digital stage, where an AGI connects humans with machines and virtual reality within the smart grid systems.
C. The 3rd stage is an ASI influencing, mobilizing, enslaving, controlling, or killing the entire human race in an extinction event or in stages without the human population realizing it in the process.

Knowing all this, a world dialogue needs to be had. As we begin to tackle these challenges before, they arise, we also need to improve our ethics on a global scale and end injustice wherever it be through a collaborative effort. Because 7.5 Billion people, with advanced technology, could spell disaster if let's say 0.1 percent of the people have ill intent or apt to do harm if their emotions get the worse of them during the course of life.

Once AI systems are connected on the 5G-6G networks, anyone, anywhere can make deadly technology with the assistance of AI apps, machines, and deep learning algorithms. This excludes whether they are connected with some sensitive AI technology or projects.

At present, the Chinese Regime (CCP) possessed the greatest threat to the world in the Great Reset, via long-term enslavement or AI-based military dominance on the BRI (Belt and Road Initiative) New

Silk Road connecting China to the Middle East, South America, Africa, and May be Europe and parts of North America in some respects.

I like to thank the reader for taking the time to read this short analytical overview of the Great Reset and ask you to urge others to get this book and Artificial Intelligence Danger to Humanity and support us in our efforts to bring a better world. I personally spent 20 hours a day, 7 days a week, prior and during the CCP Virus outbreak and during the lockdown putting out information, articles, videos, and reports to governments, media, and society in an altruistic effort to reduce damage by describing and warning in thousands of ways how the world's people were endangered from China CCP and its interconnected after-effects.

Not many believed my narrative, and not many came to support until after lockdown, deaths and financial damages were realized to stem from everything I disclosed in 2019 which was spot on factual, prior to the events CCP Virus/COVID-19 release. More so, factual in terms of emerging dangers from the described geopolitical tech dangers involving the Great Reset, and conflicts around lockdowns. Yet, intelligence agencies, and the U.S. government took notice and made huge steps.

I would like to ask for support from major players and the common persons to help shape a better world, reduce risks to the world's citizens, and enter an age of enlightenment based on free will by incorporating AI safely for liberals, conservatives, and everyone else.

Sincerely,

Cyrus A. Parsa, The AI Organization,

Front Cover

ID 179526227, Grandeduc , Dreamstime.com ,

Book Body Picture Credits, Images Courtesy of Dreamstime.com

Made in the USA
Middletown, DE
30 October 2021

51259135R00086